GCSE AQA
Additional Science
10-Minute Tests

There's a lot to learn for GCSE Additional Science... sometimes it can
be hard to get motivated for a big revision session.

That's why we've made this brilliant little book. It's packed with **30** short,
sharp tests — each one will fit into a tiny **10 minute** slice of your life.

All the answers are included, so you can find out how you did straight away!

What CGP is all about

Our sole aim here at CGP is to produce the highest
quality books — carefully written, immaculately presented
and dangerously close to being funny.

Then we work our socks off to get them
out to you — at the cheapest possible prices.

Published by CGP

Editors:
Jane Applegarth, Julie Wakeling, Dawn Wright

ISBN: 978 1 78294 456 0
Printed by Elanders Ltd, Newcastle upon Tyne
Clipart from Corel®

Based on the classic CGP style created by Richard Parsons.

Contents

B2a — Cells, Organs & Populations: Test 1

There are **12 questions** in this test. Give yourself **10 minutes** to answer them all.

1. What's the function of mesophyll tissue?

   A It covers a plant.

   B It's where photosynthesis happens.

   C It carries substances around a plant.

   [1]

2. How do plants make proteins from glucose?

   A Using photosynthesis.

   B Using respiration.

   C By combining it with nitrate ions.

   [1]

3. Which of these might make the rate of diffusion increase?

   A A greater difference in concentration between the two areas.

   B No difference in concentration between the two areas.

   [1]

4. True or False? "Quadrats can be used with transects."

   A True

   B False

   [1]

5. The distribution of an organism is…

   A … what it eats.

   B … where it's found.

   C … how many individuals there are.

   [1]

6. Which of these cells is specialised for reproduction?

   A Red blood cell

   B Guard cell

   C Egg cell

   [1]

7. True or False? "Increasing the temperature always causes the rate of photosynthesis to increase."

   A True

   B False

   [1]

8. True or False? "The starch in plants that's created from glucose is insoluble."

   A True

   B False

   [1]

9. Give one difference between a bacterial cell and a yeast cell.

   ....

   ....
   [1]

10. Explain what is meant by the term "cell differentiation".

   ....

   ....
   [1]

11. Name the supporting material that plants make using glucose.
    Which part of the cell is made using this material?

   ....

   ....
   [2]

12. Label the structures on this diagram of the digestive system.

   A ....

   B ....

   C ....
   [3]

15

4

B2a — Cells, Organs & Populations: Test 2

There are **12 questions** in this test. Give yourself **10 minutes** to answer them all.

1. Which of these things are <u>not</u> used by plants to make proteins?

   A Glucose

   B Nitrate ions

   C Lipids

   [1]

2. Palisade leaf cells are adapted for photosynthesis. Which of these characteristics would help them to carry out their specialised function?

   A Having a thick cell wall.

   B Containing lots of chloroplasts.

   C Being situated at the bottom of a leaf.

   [1]

3. What is a tissue?

   A A collection of different types of cell that work together.

   B A collection of similar cells that work together.

   [1]

4. True or False? "The amount of oxygen in the environment might affect where an organism lives."

   A True

   B False

   [1]

5. What is the function of a red blood cell?

   A To help with sexual reproduction.

   B To carry glucose to the organs.

   C To carry oxygen to the organs.

   [1]

6. Which of these parts are not found in a bacterial cell?

   A Nucleus

   B Cell membrane

   C Cell wall

   [1]

7. Diffusion is where particles spread out from…

   A … an area of low concentration to an area of high concentration.

   B … an area of high concentration to an area of low concentration.

   [1]

8. True or False? "Photosynthesis is slower at night."

   A True

   B False

   [1]

9. Explain why some dissolved substances are unable to enter cells by diffusion.

....

.... [1]

10. This diagram shows a sperm cell.
Suggest one way in which a sperm cell is
adapted to carry out its specialised function.

....

.... [1]

11. Complete the equation for photosynthesis.

....

.... + water $\longrightarrow$ .... + oxygen

[2]

12. You've counted the number of daisies in 5 sample areas using a quadrat. Describe how
you would work out:

The mean number of daisies in a quadrat.

....

....

The median number of daisies in a quadrat.

....

.... [3]

15

B2a — Cells, Organs & Populations: Test 3

There are **11 questions** in this test. Give yourself **10 minutes** to answer them all.

1. Which of these is not a limiting factor
    of photosynthesis?

    A Light

    B Temperature

    C Oxygen
    [1]

2. Where do most of the chemical reactions
    in a cell take place?

    A Mitochondria

    B Chloroplasts

    C Cytoplasm
    [1]

3. True or False? "Cells can get the substances
    they need through diffusion."

    A True

    B False
    [1]

4. True or False? "As the level of carbon
    dioxide increases, the rate of photosynthesis
    will always increase."

    A True

    B False
    [1]

5. When all the variables are controlled and
    a large sample size is used, the data is
    likely to be…

    A … reproducible and valid.

    B … reproducible but not valid.

    C … valid but not reproducible.
    [1]

6. Chloroplasts…

    A … strengthen a plant cell.

    B … store the genetic material of a cell.

    C … absorb light energy to make glucose.
    [1]

7. How are red blood cells adapted to carry out
    their function?

    A They have a convex shape.

    B They have a concave shape.
    [1]

8. True or False? "Organisms live in different
    habitats because they're better suited to
    certain environmental factors."

    A True

    B False
    [1]

9. What is the difference in the functions of the small and large intestines?

....

....

....
[2]

10. Describe what a quadrat is and suggest how one can be used.

....

....

....
[2]

11. Name three types of tissue found in the stomach, and state the function of each type.

1. ....

....

2. ....

....

3. ....

....
[3]

15

B2a — Cells, Organs & Populations: Test 4

There are **11 questions** in this test. Give yourself **10 minutes** to answer them all.

1. What is the function of cellulose?

   A To strengthen the cell walls in plants

   B To make proteins

   C To help with respiration

   [1]

2. What is the name for the process where perfume particles spread out in the air?

   A Active transport

   B Osmosis

   C Diffusion

   [1]

3. True or False? "Specialised cells only exist in animals."

   A True

   B False

   [1]

4. What is a vacuole?

   A The space in a plant cell which is filled with cell sap.

   B The space in a plant cell which contains chlorophyll.

   [1]

5. How can you make sure that data about the distribution of organisms is valid?

   A Always take the sample from the same place.

   B Control all of the variables.

   C Have a small sample size.

   [1]

6. Other than oxygen, what does photosynthesis produce?

   A Carbon dioxide

   B Water

   C Glucose

   [1]

7. True or False? "A flower might be more common in the centre of a field than next to the hedges due to the amount of light."

   A True

   B False

   [1]

8. True or False? "Organ systems work together to form organs."

   A True

   B False

   [1]

9. Describe what happens to the rate of photosynthesis in a plant as the temperature increases.

....

....

....
[2]

10. Complete this diagram of an animal cell.

Describe the roles of the following parts of a cell:

Mitochondria ....

....

Ribosomes ....

....
[4]

11. Name the process by which the oxygen needed for respiration passes through cell membranes.

....

[1]

15

B2a — Cells, Organs & Populations: Test 5

There are **12 questions** in this test. Give yourself **10 minutes** to answer them all.

1. Which of these is yeast an example of?

   A A bacterium

   B A cell without a nucleus

   C A single-celled organism

   [1]

2. What does glandular tissue do?

   A It covers parts of the body.

   B It makes and secretes chemicals.

   C It contracts to move parts of the body.

   [1]

3. True or False? "Some particles can't diffuse across a cell membrane."

   A True

   B False

   [1]

4. Some of the glucose from photosynthesis is used for…

   A … transpiration.

   B … respiration.

   [1]

5. How can you study the distribution of organisms in a way that will give reproducible results?

   A Always take the sample from the same place.

   B Use a small sample size.

   C Use a large sample size.

   [1]

6. What happens in the ribosomes in a cell?

   A Photosynthesis takes place.

   B DNA is stored.

   C Proteins are produced.

   [1]

7. What is chlorophyll used for in photosynthesis?

   A Absorbing light energy

   B Absorbing glucose

   [1]

8. True or False? "Stems, roots and leaves are all plant organs."

   A True

   B False

   [1]

9. Name two glands that are part of the digestive system.

    .... and ....
    [1]

10. Explain what happens to the rate of photosynthesis if a plant is put in a dark place.

    ....

    ....

    ....
    [2]

11. How do plants make protein?

    ....

    ....
    [2]

12. Shaun wants to study the distribution of daffodils in a field.
    Suggest how he could do this.

    ....

    ....

    ....

    ....
    [2]

B2b — Enzymes & Genetics: Test 1

There are **12 questions** in this test. Give yourself **10 minutes** to answer them all.

1. If a dog with long hair (Hh) was bred with a dog with short hair (hh), what possible combinations of alleles could be produced?

    A hh

    B HH

    C Hh, hh

    [1]

2. What do we mean by isolation in terms of populations of organisms?

    A Where a single organism gets separated from the rest of a population.

    B Where populations of the same species become separated.

    C Where a volcanic eruption wipes out all the populations of an entire species.

    [1]

3. True or False? "Fossils can be formed from the footprints and burrows of an organism that have been preserved over time."

    A True

    B False

    [1]

4. What is an organism's genotype?

    A The characteristics that the organism has.

    B The alleles that the organism has.

    [1]

5. What pH is it in the stomach?

    A pH 2

    B pH 7

    C pH 12

    [1]

6. How many chromosomes does a sperm cell contain?

    A 23

    B 46

    C 52

    [1]

7. Alex walked to catch the bus, but Peter was late so had to run. Whose heart rate will be higher?

    A Alex

    B Peter

    [1]

8. True or False? "Some people think embryo screening is ethically wrong."

    A True

    B False

    [1]

9. "Digestion is the only role played by enzymes in the body."
Explain why this statement is incorrect.

....

....
[1]

10. Describe what is meant by muscle fatigue and explain when it occurs.

....

....

....
[2]

11. Give two functions of mitosis.

1. ....

2. ....
[2]

12. Describe the idea that Mendel proposed as a result of his research on pea plants.

....

....

....

....
[2]

B2b — Enzymes & Genetics: Test 2

*There are **12 questions** in this test. Give yourself **10 minutes** to answer them all.*

1. How many cell divisions occur during meiosis?

   A 1

   B 2

   C 4

   [1]

2. What are proteins made up of?

   A Long chains of glucose molecules

   B Long chains of fatty acids

   C Long chains of amino acids

   [1]

3. True or False? "Fossils can help to show us how species have evolved."

   A True

   B False

   [1]

4. True or False? "Enzymes can usually catalyse many different types of reaction."

   A True

   B False

   [1]

5. Where is bile produced and stored?

   A Bile is produced in the liver and stored in the gall bladder.

   B Bile is produced in the gall bladder and stored in the stomach.

   C Bile is produced in the stomach and stored in the pancreas.

   [1]

6. What structure does DNA have?

   A A long, single, straight chain

   B A triple helix structure

   C A double helix structure

   [1]

7. True or False? "It's completely random which organisms survive and pass on their genes to the next generation."

   A True

   B False

   [1]

8. True or False? "Stem cell research is banned in the UK."

   A True

   B False

   [1]

9. Which sex chromosome causes male characteristics to develop?

....
[1]

10. Give two factors that might cause a species to become extinct.

1. ....

....

2. ....

....
[2]

11. A tall pea plant with two dominant 'T' alleles and a dwarf pea plant with two recessive 't' alleles are crossed to produce a pea plant with the genotype Tt. What will the new plant's phenotype be? Explain your answer.

....

....

....

....
[2]

12. What is DNA fingerprinting?

....

....

....
[2]

15

B2b — Enzymes & Genetics: Test 3

There are **12 questions** in this test. Give yourself **10 minutes** to answer them all.

1. Which of the following doesn't produce amylase?

   A The salivary glands

   B The pancreas

   C The stomach

   [1]

2. What is a gene?

   A An amino acid

   B A protein

   C A small section of DNA

   [1]

3. True or False? "Anaerobic respiration requires oxygen."

   A True

   B False

   [1]

4. True or False? "The optimum pH for all enzymes to work is pH 7."

   A True

   B False

   [1]

5. What sex chromosomes does a male have?

   A XY

   B XXX

   C XX

   [1]

6. Gregor Mendel was an Austrian monk who…

   A … discovered that men have a Y chromosome.

   B … showed that embryonic stem cells can differentiate into any type of cell.

   C …. investigated how pea plants pass on their characteristics from one generation to the next.

   [1]

7. True or False? "Aerobic respiration occurs in plants and animals all the time."

   A True

   B False

   [1]

8. Which type of cell division produces gametes?

   A Meiosis

   B Mitosis

   [1]

9. Describe what happens to an enzyme if the temperature is too high.

    ....

    ....

    ....
    [2]

10. What is meant by embryo screening?

    ....

    ....
    [1]

11. What is a fossil?

    ....

    ....
    [1]

12. Explain why speciation might occur if two populations of the same species are isolated
    from one another by a flood.

    ....

    ....

    ....

    ....

    ....
    [3]

15

B2b — Enzymes & Genetics: Test 4

*There are **11 questions** in this test. Give yourself **10 minutes** to answer them all.*

1. Where in a cell do most of the reactions involved in aerobic respiration take place?

   A The cytoplasm

   B The nucleus

   C The mitochondria

   [1]

2. What are Mendel's 'hereditary units' now known as?

   A Genes

   B Ribosomes

   C Mitochondria

   [1]

3. True or False? "The alleles for cystic fibrosis and polydactyly are both dominant."

   A True

   B False

   [1]

4. The role of digestive enzymes is to…

   A … catalyse the breakdown of large molecules into smaller molecules.

   B … catalyse the formation of large molecules from smaller ones.

   [1]

5. What happens to enzymes at high temperatures?

   A They divide, producing more enzymes

   B They start to attack the cells in the body

   C They denature

   [1]

6. Which of the following doesn't use mitosis?

   A Asexual reproduction

   B Producing gametes

   C Replacing damaged cells

   [1]

7. True or False? "DNA fingerprinting is a technique that can be used to identify different individuals."

   A True

   B False

   [1]

8. If a plant has both the dominant and recessive 'hereditary unit' for a characteristic, which will be displayed by the plant?

   A The dominant characteristic

   B The recessive characteristic

   [1]

9. Rachael and Henry are about to have a child. Both of them carry the cystic fibrosis gene, but are not sufferers.
Complete the genetic diagram to show the possible genotypes of the child.

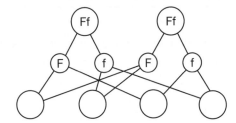

What is the chance that their child will suffer from the condition?
Explain your answer.

....

....

....
[3]

10. In terms of populations, describe what is meant by the term isolation.

....

....
[1]

11. Give three arguments for using embryos in stem cell research.

1. ....

   ....

2. ....

   ....

3. ....

   ....
[3]

15

B2b — Enzymes & Genetics: Test 5

There are **12 questions** in this test. Give yourself **10 minutes** to answer them all.

1. Why is the shape of an enzyme important for its function?

   A So that it can squeeze through small gaps.

   B So that it can enter the cells of the body.

   C So that it fits the substance involved in the reaction it is catalysing.

   [1]

2. How many gametes are produced when one starting cell completes meiosis?

   A 2

   B 4

   C 6

   [1]

3. True or False? "Each gene codes for a specific lipid."

   A True

   B False

   [1]

4. True or False? "Chromosomes are normally found in pairs in body cells."

   A True

   B False

   [1]

5. What are alleles?

   A Male sex chromosomes

   B Two gametes fused together

   C Different versions of the same gene

   [1]

6. During exercise, which of the following happens?

   A Just the rate of your breathing increases.

   B Just the depth of your breathing increases.

   C The rate and depth of your breathing increases.

   [1]

7. At which temperatures are biological detergents more effective than other detergents?

   A Low temperatures

   B High temperatures

   [1]

8. True or False? "All plant cells lose the ability to differentiate at an early stage."

   A True

   B False

   [1]

9. Alex has an X chromosome and a Y chromosome. Is Alex a boy or a girl?

....
[1]

10. What is the role of protease enzymes in the stomach?

....

....
[1]

11. Give two uses of the energy produced by respiration.

1. ....

....

2. ....

....
[2]

12. Explain how sexual reproduction produces variation.

....

....

....

....

....
[3]

15

C2a — Bonding & Calculations: Test 1

There are **11 questions** in this test. Give yourself **10 minutes** to answer them all.

1. What is the overall charge on an ionic compound?

   A 0

   B −1

   C +1

   [1]

2. What type of bond is formed when two hydrogen atoms form a molecule?

   A An ionic bond

   B A covalent bond

   C A compound bond

   [1]

3. True or False? "Pure metals are harder than alloys."

   A True

   B False

   [1]

4. True or False? "Simple molecular substances have high boiling points."

   A True

   B False

   [1]

5. What is the yield of a reaction?

   A The mass of reactants used in a reaction.

   B The temperature of a product.

   C The amount of product obtained.

   [1]

6. Thermosetting polymers have…

   A … polymer chains with cross-links.

   B … tangled polymer chains.

   C … weak intermolecular forces.

   [1]

7. What is a reversible reaction?

   A A reaction where the products of the reaction can react to produce further products.

   B A reaction where the products of the reaction can react to produce the original reactants.

   [1]

8. True or False? "H_2O is a giant ionic substance."

   A True

   B False

   [1]

9. Name the type of structure shown in the diagram:

....
[1]

10. Mg has a relative atomic mass of 24, O has a relative atomic mass of 16
    and H has a relative atomic mass of 1.

    Work out the number of moles in 145 g of $Mg(OH)_2$.
    (Number of moles = Mass ÷ M_r)

    ....

    ....

    ....

    .... moles
    [3]

11. Describe the structure of fullerenes. Give one example of their use.

    ....

    ....

    ....

    ....

    ....
    [3]

15

C2a — Bonding & Calculations: Test 2

There are **11 questions** in this test. Give yourself **10 minutes** to answer them all.

1. If the relative atomic mass of H = 1 and O = 16, what is the relative formula mass of H_2O?

    A 17

    B 18

    C 34

    [1]

2. What is nitinol?

    A A thermosetting polymer

    B A nanoparticle

    C A shape memory alloy

    [1]

3. True or False? "Isotopes of an element have the same atomic number but different mass numbers."

    A True

    B False

    [1]

4. True or False? "Gas chromatography can be linked to mass spectroscopy."

    A True

    B False

    [1]

5. An ionic compound is made up of Na^+ ions and Br^- ions. What is its formula?

    A NaBr

    B Na_2Br

    C $NaBr_2$

    [1]

6. Fluorine is in Group 7 of the periodic table. What is the charge on a fluoride ion?

    A 1+

    B 1–

    C 2–

    [1]

7. True or False? "Low density and high density poly(ethene) are made using the same catalyst."

    A True

    B False

    [1]

8. Giant covalent structures have…

    A … low melting points.

    B … high melting points.

    [1]

9. Describe the relative masses of protons, neutrons and electrons in an atom.

    ....

    ....
    [1]

10. Describe the structure of an ionic compound. What holds it together?

    ....

    ....

    ....

    ....
    [3]

11. Carbon (C) has a relative atomic mass of 12, oxygen (O) has a relative atomic mass of
    16 and hydrogen (H) has a relative atomic mass of 1.

    Calculate the percentage mass of carbon in $C_2H_5(OH)$.
    Give your answer rounded to the nearest whole number.

    ....

    ....

    ....

    ....

    .... %
    [3]

15

C2a — Bonding & Calculations: Test 3

*There are **11 questions** in this test. Give yourself **10 minutes** to answer them all.*

1. What holds the oppositely charged ions together in ionic lattices?

   A   Covalent bonds

   B   Electrostatic forces

   C   Delocalised electrons

   [1]

2. Beryllium is in Group 2 of the periodic table. What is the charge on a beryllium ion?

   A   1–

   B   1+

   C   2+

   [1]

3. True or False? "Atoms of the same element can have different numbers of neutrons."

   A   True

   B   False

   [1]

4. True or False? "Ionic compounds conduct electricity when dissolved in water but not when molten."

   A   True

   B   False

   [1]

5. Which of these will not affect the properties of a polymer?

   A   The catalyst used in its production.

   B   The reaction conditions during its production.

   C   The quantity made during production.

   [1]

6. In simple molecular substances…

   A   … the intermolecular forces are much stronger than the covalent bonds within the molecules.

   B   … the covalent bonds within the molecules are much stronger than the intermolecular forces.

   C   … the covalent bonds within the molecules are the same strength as the intermolecular forces.

   [1]

7. True or False? "In reversible reactions, the reactants never fully convert to the products."

   A   True

   B   False

   [1]

8. True or False? "Pure metals can be bent because the layers of atoms can slide over each other."

   A   True

   B   False

   [1]

9. Describe the bonding in a Cl_2 molecule.

....

....

....

....

[2]

10. 66 g of carbon ($A_r = 12$) are burnt completely in oxygen ($A_r = 16$) to produce CO_2.

Calculate the mass of CO_2 produced.

....

....

....

....

.... g

[3]

11. What are nanoparticles? Give one example of where they can be used.

....

....

....

....

[2]

15

C2a — Bonding & Calculations: Test 4

*There are **11 questions** in this test. Give yourself **10 minutes** to answer them all.*

1. What is a covalent bond?

   A A pair of electrons shared between two atoms.

   B A pair of electrons transferred from one atom to another.

   C An attraction between two oppositely charged ions.

   [1]

2. The relative atomic mass of an element compares the mass of atoms of that element with the mass of an atom of…

   A … carbon-11.

   B … carbon-12.

   C … carbon-13.

   [1]

3. True or False? "All covalent substances have a macromolecular structure."

   A True

   B False

   [1]

4. True or False? "Nanoparticles can be used in cosmetics."

   A True

   B False

   [1]

5. Which of these describes a metallic structure?

   A A giant structure of metal atoms held together by ionic bonds.

   B A giant structure of metal atoms arranged in an irregular pattern.

   C A giant structure of metal atoms arranged in a regular pattern.

   [1]

6. Which of these can be used to detect whether foods contain artificial colours?

   A Indicator strips

   B Limewater

   C Paper chromatography

   [1]

7. The number of peaks on a gas chromatograph indicates…

   A … the number of compounds present.

   B … the retention time.

   [1]

8. True or False? "You can calculate the empirical formula of a compound using either the masses or percentages of the elements in the compound."

   A True

   B False

   [1]

9. What are isotopes?

....

....
$\qquad$ *[1]*

10. The predicted yield of product X from a reaction is 50 g. The actual yield is 36 g.

Calculate the percentage yield of product X, and suggest one reason
why it is less than 100%.

....

Percentage yield = ... %

....

....
$\qquad$ *[3]*

11. Explain, in terms of their different structures, why oxygen does not conduct electricity,
but graphite does.

....

....

....

....

....
$\qquad$ *[3]*

15

C2a — Bonding & Calculations: Test 5

There are **10 questions** in this test. Give yourself **10 minutes** to answer them all.

1. CH_4 and Cl_2 are…

    A … simple molecules.

    B … macromolecules.

    C … giant covalent structures.

    [1]

2. What name is given to the total number of protons and neutrons in an atom?

    A Atomic mass

    B Atomic number

    C Mass number

    [1]

3. True or False? "The percentage yield always depends on the amount of reactants you start with."

    A True

    B False

    [1]

4. True or False? "The way polymers are made affects the properties they have."

    A True

    B False

    [1]

5. What is nitinol used for?

    A Making fullerenes

    B Making cosmetics

    C Dental braces

    [1]

6. What type of structure does silicon dioxide have?

    A Simple molecular

    B Macromolecular

    C Ionic lattice

    [1]

7. True or False? "Nanoparticles have different properties from much larger amounts of the same material."

    A True

    B False

    [1]

8. Why do ionic compounds have high boiling points?

    A The bonds between the ions are weak but there are strong intermolecular forces.

    B It takes a lot of energy to break the bonds between the ions.

    [1]

9. Iron (Fe) has a relative atomic mass of 56.
   Oxygen (O) has a relative atomic mass of 16.

   Find the empirical formula of the iron oxide produced when 140 g of iron react
   with 40 g of oxygen.

   ....

   ....

   ....

   ....

   ....
   [3]

10. Describe the process of using gas chromatography linked to mass spectroscopy
    (GC-MS) to identify different substances carried by a gas.

    ....

    ....

    ....

    ....

    ....

    ....

    ....

    ....
    [4]

15

C2b — Rates, Salts & Electrolysis: Test 1

There are **11 questions** in this test. Give yourself **10 minutes** to answer them all.

1. The rate of a reaction depends on the…

   A … frequency of collisions.

   B … volume of solutions.

   C … location of the experiment.

       [1]

2. Which of these is a disadvantage of using catalysts?

   A They are often expensive to buy.

   B They can't be reused.

   C They slow down reactions too much.

       [1]

3. True or False? "H^+ ions are oxidised during the electrolysis of sodium hydroxide solution."

   A True

   B False

       [1]

4. Which of these reactions would be faster?

   A Magnesium with concentrated acid

   B Magnesium with dilute acid

       [1]

5. What is the activation energy of a reaction?

   A The amount of energy used to start a reaction.

   B The minimum amount of energy needed by the particles to react.

   C The maximum amount of energy needed by the particles to react.

       [1]

6. What is the problem with using acids and alkalis to make soluble salts?

   A Acids and alkalis don't react together.

   B Acids and alkalis explode when they're put together.

   C It can be hard to tell when the acid and alkali have finished reacting.

       [1]

7. True or False? "Energy is always transferred to or from the surroundings during a chemical reaction."

   A True

   B False

       [1]

8. True or False? "Electroplating is used to manufacture aluminium from aluminium oxide."

   A True

   B False

       [1]

9. The diagram shows the results of the same reaction carried out in two different experiments.

   Suggest one way in which the conditions might have been different in experiment 2. Explain your answer.

   ....

   ....

   ....

   [2]

10. State the two products formed in a reaction between a metal and an acid.

    1. ....

    2. ....

    [2]

11. Is thermal decomposition exothermic or endothermic? Explain your answer.

    ....

    ....

    ....

    ....

    ....

    [3]

15

C2b — Rates, Salts & Electrolysis: Test 2

*There are **12 questions** in this test. Give yourself **10 minutes** to answer them all.*

1. In electrolysis, the electrolyte must be a…

   A … solid.

   B ... liquid.

   C ... gas.

   [1]

2. Why is cryolite used during the production of aluminium from its oxide by electrolysis?

   A It lowers the melting point of aluminium oxide.

   B It increases the melting point of aluminium.

   C It increases the temperature.

   [1]

3. True or False? "Rate of reaction can be found using either the amount of reactant used or the amount of product formed over a period of time."

   A True

   B False

   [1]

4. True or False? "A reversible reaction always takes in more energy in one direction than it gives out in the opposite direction."

   A True

   B False

   [1]

5. Which of these could you use to make the salt lead chloride?

   A Lead nitrate and magnesium sulfate

   B Lead nitrate and zinc sulfate

   C Lead nitrate and sodium chloride

   [1]

6. Which of these uses an endothermic reaction?

   A Hand warmers

   B Sports injury packs

   C Self heating cans for drinks

   [1]

7. True or False? "Oxidation reactions always involve oxygen."

   A True

   B False

   [1]

8. True or False? "Sulfuric acid and aluminium react to produce aluminium sulfate and oxygen."

   A True

   B False

   [1]

9. Give the equation for the reaction between hydrogen ions and hydroxide ions during a neutralisation reaction.

....
[1]

10. What is the difference between an alkali and a base?

....

....
[1]

11. Name the two gases formed in the electrolysis of sodium chloride.

1. ....

2. ....
[2]

12. Explain, using collision theory, why increasing the concentration of a reactant solution increases the rate of a reaction.

....

....

....

....

....
[3]

15

C2b — Rates, Salts & Electrolysis: Test 3

*There are **11 questions** in this test. Give yourself **10 minutes** to answer them all.*

1. Electrolysis of sodium chloride produces sodium hydroxide solution. What can the sodium hydroxide be used to make?

    A Ammonia

    B Soap

    C Cryolite
    [1]

2. How can a solid salt be obtained from a salt solution?

    A By adding an indicator.

    B By adding a catalyst.

    C By crystallisation of the salt solution.
    [1]

3. True or False? "Catalysts are used up during a reaction."

    A True

    B False
    [1]

4. True or False? "Chemical reactions all happen at the same speed."

    A True

    B False
    [1]

5. What is the pH scale used to measure?

    A The mass of a solution.

    B The temperature of a solution.

    C How acidic or alkaline a solution is.
    [1]

6. If the concentration of a reactant in a solution is doubled, the solution…

    A … contains more reactant particles.

    B … contains fewer reactant particles.

    C … takes up more room.
    [1]

7. What is an exothermic reaction?

    A A reaction which transfers energy to the surroundings.

    B A reaction which takes in energy from the surroundings.
    [1]

8. True or False? "An indicator can be used to find when an acid and an alkali have completely reacted in a neutralisation reaction."

    A True

    B False
    [1]

9. Name the two products formed in the reaction between hydrochloric acid and copper oxide.

    1. ....

    2. ....

[2]

10. Describe what happens in a precipitation reaction.

    ....

    ....

    ....

[2]

11. A solid reacts with a solution to form a gas.
    Describe one way of finding the rate of this reaction.

    ....

    ....

    ....

    ....

    ....

[3]

15

C2b — Rates, Salts & Electrolysis: Test 4

*There are **11 questions** in this test. Give yourself **10 minutes** to answer them all.*

1. What does a pH of 7 indicate?

    A An acidic solution

    B An alkaline solution

    C A neutral solution

    [1]

2. In a reaction between marble and hydrochloric acid, using small marble chips instead of a large piece of marble will produce…

    A … no difference in the rate of reaction.

    B … a faster rate of reaction.

    C … a slower rate of reaction.

    [1]

3. True or False? "In a gaseous reaction mixture, increasing the pressure increases the reaction rate."

    A True

    B False

    [1]

4. True or False? "A base that won't dissolve in water will still react with an acid."

    A True

    B False

    [1]

5. What solution is produced by the electrolysis of sodium chloride?

    A Sodium chloride

    B Sodium oxide

    C Sodium hydroxide

    [1]

6. What is electroplating?

    A Removing the surface of a metal object.

    B Coating an object with a thin layer of metal.

    C Creating an electric plate.

    [1]

7. True or False? "Hydroxide ions make solutions acidic."

    A True

    B False

    [1]

8. True or False? "Hydrochloric acid and magnesium react to produce magnesium chloride and hydrogen."

    A True

    B False

    [1]

9. Name the type of reaction that occurs between an acid and an alkali, and state the two
    products that are formed.

    ....

    ....
    [2]

10. Give two ways in which catalysts can reduce costs when used in industrial reactions.

    1. ....

        ....

    2. ....

        ....
        [2]

11. Describe how ammonia can be used to make fertiliser.

    ....

    ....

    ....

    ....

    ....
    [3]

15

C2b — Rates, Salts & Electrolysis: Test 5

There are **11 questions** in this test. Give yourself **10 minutes** to answer them all.

1. Which of these methods can be used to make an insoluble salt?

   A Precipitation

   B Electroplating

   C Fermentation

   [1]

2. In electrolysis, at the negative electrode, positively charged ions…

   A … lose electrons.

   B … gain electrons.

   C … dissolve.

   [1]

3. True or False? "Increasing the pressure of any reaction mixture will increase the reaction rate."

   A True

   B False

   [1]

4. True or False? "A solution with a pH of 1 is very acidic."

   A True

   B False

   [1]

5. An alkaline solution of ammonia reacts with nitric acid to produce…

   A … carbon dioxide.

   B … ammonium metals.

   C … ammonium salts.

   [1]

6. Why does increasing the temperature increase the rate of a reaction?

   A The reactant particles evaporate to form a gas.

   B The reactant particles move faster so they collide more frequently.

   C The reactant particles stick together more.

   [1]

7. True or False? "The same catalyst can be used in all reactions."

   A True

   B False

   [1]

8. Which of these is a property of a soluble salt?

   A It can dissolve in water.

   B It can't dissolve in water.

   [1]

9. Describe the difference between oxidation and reduction in terms of electrons.

....

....
[1]

10. The equation for the decomposition of hydrogen peroxide is shown below:

$2H_2O_{2(aq)} \rightarrow 2H_2O_{(l)} + O_{2(g)}$

Explain how the total volume of O_2 produced is affected by the presence of a catalyst.

....

....

....
[2]

11. Aluminium can be extracted from a solution of aluminium oxide in molten cryolite using electrolysis. Describe what happens at the electrodes during this process.

....

....

....

....

....

....
[4]

15

P2a — Motion, Energy & Electricity: Test 1

There are **11 questions** in this test. Give yourself **10 minutes** to answer them all.

1. How does the speed of a car affect its stopping distance at maximum braking force?

   A Higher speed results in a shorter stopping distance.

   B Higher speed results in a longer stopping distance.

   C The speed of the car doesn't matter.

   [1]

2. Static electricity is caused by the movement of which particles?

   A Electrons

   B Neutrons

   C Protons

   [1]

3. True or False? "Momentum depends on the direction of travel."

   A True

   B False

   [1]

4. True or False? "If something's moving there must be an overall resultant force on it."

   A True

   B False

   [1]

5. In which direction does friction act compared to an object's movement?

   A Perpendicular (at right angles)

   B The same direction

   C The opposite direction

   [1]

6. Which of these does not lessen the force on passengers during a car crash?

   A Crumple zones

   B Seat belts

   C Regenerative brakes

   [1]

7. When an object falls from a height, the kinetic energy gained is equal to...

   A ... the potential energy gained.

   B ... the potential energy lost.

   [1]

8. True or False? "In a parallel circuit, each component always has the same potential difference across it."

   A True

   B False

   [1]

9. Look at this graph.

   Describe the motion of the object between points A and C.

   ....

   ....

   ....
   [2]

10. Give one similarity and one difference between an LDR and a thermistor.

   ....

   ....

   ....
   [2]

11. A robot has a power output of 50 W. How much energy does it transfer in 2 minutes?

   power = energy transferred ÷ time taken

   ....

   ....

   ....

   .... J
   [3]

   15

P2a — Motion, Energy & Electricity: Test 2

*There are **11 questions** in this test. Give yourself **10 minutes** to answer them all.*

---

1. A teapot, weighing 10 N, is sat stationary on a table. What's the upwards force applied to it by the table?

    A 0 N

    B 10 N

    C 20 N

    [1]

2. Brakes heat up when they're used because...

    A ... thermal energy is converted to kinetic energy.

    B ... kinetic energy is converted to thermal energy.

    C ... kinetic energy is gained.

    [1]

3. Opening a parachute...

    A ... increases a skydiver's upwards drag.

    B ... decreases a skydiver's upwards drag.

    [1]

4. True or False? "When two conducting materials are rubbed against each other, a static charge can build up."

    A True

    B False

    [1]

5. The acceleration of an object is...

    A ... the change in height over time.

    B ... the change in position over time.

    C ... the change in velocity over time.

    [1]

6. In a car's parallel electrical circuit, each component will usually receive...

    A ... a small part of the supply potential difference.

    B ... the same current as any other component.

    C ... the full supply potential difference.

    [1]

7. True or False? "A voltmeter must be placed in series with the component under test in a circuit."

    A True

    B False

    [1]

8. In a closed system, the total momentum before a collision is...

    A ... the same as the total momentum after the collision.

    B ... always zero.

    [1]

9. A skater with a mass of 60 kg pushes against a wall and accelerates backwards at 3 m/s². What force did she push with?

resultant force = mass × acceleration

....

.... N
[1]

10. Explain how and why an object's speed changes as it falls through a fluid from rest.

....

....

....

....
[3]

11. This potential difference-current graph is for a filament lamp.

Explain why the graph curves as the current increases.

....

....

....

....
[3]

15

P2a — Motion, Energy & Electricity: Test 3

*There are **11 questions** in this test. Give yourself **10 minutes** to answer them all.*

1. The extension of an elastic object is...

   A ... directly proportional to the force applied.

   B ... inversely proportional to the force applied.

   C ... unrelated to the force applied.

   [1]

2. To travel at terminal velocity, the driving force of a car engine must...

   A ... be less than the frictional forces.

   B ... balance the frictional forces.

   C ... exceed the frictional forces.

   [1]

3. True or False? "If a moving object doubles its speed, it doubles its kinetic energy."

   A True

   B False

   [1]

4. True or False? "The resistance of a thermistor is higher in hot conditions than in the cold."

   A True

   B False

   [1]

5. When an object falls, some of its kinetic energy is converted to other forms of energy. Which of these is it not converted to?

   A Gravitational potential

   B Heat

   C Sound

   [1]

6. Power is the...

   A ... conservation of momentum.

   B ... energy of a moving object.

   C ... rate of doing work.

   [1]

7. True or False? "The mass of a man is greater on Earth than it is on the Moon."

   A True

   B False

   [1]

8. When two objects interact, the forces they exert on each other are...

   A ... equal and opposite.

   B ... equal and in the same direction.

   [1]

9. The graph below is incomplete. It shows the motion of a cyclist.

   Complete the graph to show the following motion:

   "Between points A and B, the cyclist's velocity increases from zero, with a gradually decreasing acceleration.
   Between points B and C, the cyclist moves at a constant velocity."

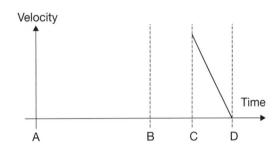

[2]

10. A 500 g object falls off a cliff and loses 100 J of gravitational potential energy.
    If g = 10 N/kg, how high is the cliff?

    change in gravitational potential energy = mass × g × change in height

    ....

    ....

    ....

    .... m

    [3]

11. A car's headlights are connected in parallel.
    Why don't both lights go out when one bulb blows?

    ....

    ....

    ....

    [2]

    15

48

*There are **11 questions** in this test. Give yourself **10 minutes** to answer them all.*

1. What effect does the speed of an object have on the drag (friction) it experiences?

   A Higher speed results in lower drag.

   B Higher speed results in higher drag.

   C It doesn't make a difference.

   [1]

2. In a circuit with a fixed potential difference, what would happen to the current if you increased the resistance?

   A The current would increase.

   B The current would stay the same.

   C The current would decrease.

   [1]

3. True or False? "The condition of the tyres affects the braking distance of a car."

   A True

   B False

   [1]

4. If the resultant force on a moving object is zero, the object will…

   A … slow down and eventually stop.

   B … keep moving at a steady speed.

   [1]

5. Regenerative brakes convert the car's kinetic energy into electrical energy, and then store it as…

   A … chemical energy.

   B … thermal (heat) energy.

   C … kinetic energy.

   [1]

6. If an object changes momentum very quickly, the forces on the object will be...

   A ... large.

   B ... small.

   C ... unrelated to the speed of the momentum change.

   [1]

7. True or False? "Potential difference is the work done per ampere of current passing between two points."

   A True

   B False

   [1]

8. True or False? "Work and energy are both measured in the same units."

   A True

   B False

   [1]

9. The circuit diagram below shows two resistors connected in series with a battery.

$$\text{potential difference} = \text{current} \times \text{resistance}$$

Find the reading on voltmeter V_3.

.... V

Find the total resistance, R, of the circuit.

.... Ω

Find the reading on ammeter A.

....

.... A
[4]

$R_1 = 6\ \Omega$ $R_2 = 4\ \Omega$

$V_1 = 3$ V $V_2 = 2$ V

10. An object feels a driving force of 1000 N, and resistance forces of 400 N in the opposite direction. What is the resultant force on the object?

....

.... N
[1]

11. This distance-time graph shows the motion of a toy car.

Distance (m)

Time (s)

Calculate the velocity of the car between points A and B.

....

....

.... m/s
[2]

15

P2a — Motion, Energy & Electricity: Test 5

There are **11 questions** in this test. Give yourself **10 minutes** to answer them all.

1. Which of the following is a device that emits light?

   A LDE

   B LED

   C LDR

   [1]

2. The maximum force an elastic object can take and still extend proportionally is known as...

   A ... the spring constant.

   B ... the limit of elasticity.

   C ... the limit of proportionality.

   [1]

3. True or False? "In a series circuit, each component always has the same potential difference across it."

   A True

   B False

   [1]

4. Speed is a measure of...

   A ... how fast something's going, regardless of direction.

   B ... how fast something's going in a given direction.

   [1]

5. What does the gradient of a distance-time graph show?

   A Acceleration

   B Distance

   C Speed

   [1]

6. Which of these is false?

   A When an object falls, work is done against gravity.

   B When an object falls, it loses gravitational potential energy.

   C When an object is lifted, work is done against gravity.

   [1]

7. Car safety features are designed to convert the kinetic energy lost in a crash...

   A ... over shorter periods of time.

   B ... over longer periods of time.

   [1]

8. True or False? "If an object's slowing down, there must be a non-zero resultant force acting on it."

   A True

   B False

   [1]

9. A stationary gun is fired, as shown in the diagram.

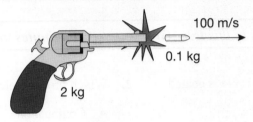

momentum = mass × velocity

What is the recoil speed of the gun?

....

....

....

....

.... m/s
[4]

10. Describe the build-up of static electricity when two insulating materials are rubbed together.

....

....

....
[2]

11. Other than increasing the engine power, how can you increase the top speed of a car?

....

....
[1]

15

P2b — Electricity & the Atom: Test 1

There are **12 questions** in this test. Give yourself **10 minutes** to answer them all.

1. Which wire inside a three-core cable is coated with blue plastic?

    A Earth

    B Live

    C Neutral

    [1]

2. Which process releases energy in stars?

    A Combustion

    B Nuclear fission

    C Nuclear fusion

    [1]

3. True or False? "People living in different parts of the UK will be exposed to different amounts of background radiation."

    A True

    B False

    [1]

4. True or False? "Isotopes that emit beta radiation can be used as tracers because beta radiation can't pass out of the body."

    A True

    B False

    [1]

5. What is the name for electric current that is constantly changing direction?

    A Alternating current (a.c.)

    B Direct current (d.c.)

    C Switching current (s.c.)

    [1]

6. What is the name for atoms with the same number of protons but different numbers of neutrons?

    A Ions

    B Isomers

    C Isotopes

    [1]

7. True or False? "Any exposure to ionising radiation will kill living cells."

    A True

    B False

    [1]

8. True or False? "Double insulated appliances must have an earth wire."

    A True

    B False

    [1]

9. Describe how a Residual Current Circuit Breaker works.

....

....

....

[2]

10. On this oscilloscope trace, the timebase is set to 0.005 s/div.

Calculate the frequency of the supply shown.

....

....

....

.... Hz

[3]

11. Which type(s) of ionising radiation are deflected by magnetic fields?

....

[1]

12. What is the difference between an atom and an ion?

....

....

[1]

15

P2b — Electricity & the Atom: Test 2

There are **11 questions** in this test. Give yourself **10 minutes** to answer them all.

1. What causes the wire inside a filament bulb to heat up when electrical charge flows through it?

   A Fluorescence

   B Insulation

   C Resistance

   [1]

2. What causes a fuse to melt inside a plug?

   A A current lower than the fuse rating.

   B A current higher than the fuse rating.

   C An alternating current.

   [1]

3. Which of these is the most dangerous outside the body?

   A Alpha radiation

   B Gamma radiation

   [1]

4. True or False? "The results of the Rutherford and Marsden scattering experiments helped them to come up with the plum pudding model of the atom."

   A True

   B False

   [1]

5. The count rate of a radioactive sample falls from 60 Bq to 30 Bq in 15 minutes. What is its half-life?

   A 15 minutes

   B 30 minutes

   C 1 hour

   [1]

6. A star much bigger than the Sun is in the 'main sequence' stage of its life. What will it become next?

   A A Red Giant

   B A Red Super Giant

   C A Supernova

   [1]

7. What is it called when two small nuclei join together?

   A Fission

   B Fusion

   [1]

8. True or False? "The higher the radiation dose you receive, the lower the chance of it causing cancer."

   A True

   B False

   [1]

9. Suggest two different ways that sources of gamma radiation can be used in hospitals.

1. ....

2. ....

[2]

10. Calculate the energy transferred (in joules) by a 15 W light bulb in 2 hours.

power = energy transferred ÷ time

....

....

....

....

.... J

[3]

11. The decay of phosphorus-32 is shown below.

$$^{32}_{15}P \rightarrow\ ^{......}_{......}S\ + \text{beta particle}$$

Complete the equation by writing in the missing atomic number and mass number of the product.

[2]

15

P2b — Electricity & the Atom: Test 3

There are **11 questions** in this test. Give yourself **10 minutes** to answer them all.

1. Which of these fuses would you fit on an appliance rated at 5 A?

    A 3 A

    B 5 A

    C 7 A

    [1]

2. What fuel is used by the majority of nuclear reactors?

    A Uranium-235

    B Uranium-325

    C Uranium-352

    [1]

3. True or False? "The plum pudding model suggested that an atom was a sphere of positively charged mass with small negative electrons stuck in it."

    A True

    B False

    [1]

4. True or False? "The UK mains electricity supply is direct current."

    A True

    B False

    [1]

5. Which of these is a use of gamma radiation?

    A Cooking food

    B Growing food

    C Sterilising food

    [1]

6. Which type of radiation is the same as a helium nucleus?

    A Alpha

    B Beta

    C Gamma

    [1]

7. True or False? "The life cycle of a star depends on its size."

    A True

    B False

    [1]

8. True or False? "The older a radioactive sample becomes, the more radiation it will emit."

    A True

    B False

    [1]

9. Use this graph to work out the half-life of the radioactive sample.

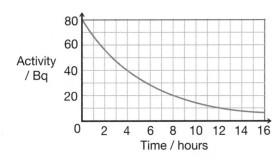

....
[2]

10. A bulb wired to a 1.5 V cell transfers 3 kJ of energy.
    How much charge passed through the bulb?

    energy = potential difference × charge

    ....

    ....

    ....

    C
    [3]

11. Describe two problems with generating electricity by nuclear fission.

    1. ....

        ....

    2. ....

        ....
        [2]

15

P2b — Electricity & the Atom: Test 4

There are **11 questions** in this test. Give yourself **10 minutes** to answer them all.

1. Which of these is caused by high doses of radiation?

   A Radioactive sickness

   B Radiation sickness

   C Radiography sickness

   [1]

2. Which type of radiation is used in smoke detectors?

   A Alpha

   B Beta

   C Gamma

   [1]

3. True or False? "Circuit breakers are better than fuses because they're cheaper."

   A True

   B False

   [1]

4. Which process is currently used to generate electricity in nuclear power stations?

   A Nuclear fission

   B Nuclear fusion

   [1]

5. Which type of radiation can penetrate the furthest into materials?

   A Alpha

   B Beta

   C Gamma

   [1]

6. Which of these is a natural source of background radiation?

   A Cosmic rays

   B Nuclear fallout

   C Nuclear waste

   [1]

7. True or False? "Rubber and plastic are used to cover wires because they are good insulators."

   A True

   B False

   [1]

8. True or False? "An atom with no overall charge is called an ion."

   A True

   B False

   [1]

9. The diagram below shows the paths of an alpha particle, a beta particle and a gamma ray through a magnetic field. Label each path with the correct radiation.

1. ....

2. ....

3. ....

[2]

10. Explain how stars stay stable for a long period of time in their main sequence phase.

....

....

....

[2]

11. Hair straighteners rated at 150 W are plugged into a 230 V mains supply.
Will a 1 A fuse be suitable? Show your working.

power = current × potential difference

....

....

....

....

[3]

15

P2b — Electricity & the Atom: Test 5

There are **11 questions** in this test. Give yourself **10 minutes** to answer them all.

1. What particle must be absorbed by a uranium or plutonium nucleus for fission to occur?

   A Electron

   B Neutron

   C Proton

   [1]

2. Which of these is not found in the nucleus of an atom?

   A Electrons

   B Neutrons

   C Protons

   [1]

3. True or False? "Two isotopes will have the same number of neutrons but a different number of protons."

   A True

   B False

   [1]

4. What type of current do cells and batteries supply?

   A Alternating current (a.c.)

   B Direct current (d.c.)

   [1]

5. Which type of radiation is used to treat cancer?

   A Alpha

   B Beta

   C Gamma

   [1]

6. Which type of radiation is the most dangerous inside the body?

   A Alpha

   B Beta

   C Gamma

   [1]

7. True or False? "All the elements found on Earth are formed during the stable period of a star's life."

   A True

   B False

   [1]

8. True or False? "An appliance with a metal case will have an earth wire."

   A True

   B False

   [1]

9. A radioactive sample has a count rate of 600 Bq. Its half-life is 30 minutes.
How long it will take for the count rate to drop to 75 Bq?

....

....

....

.... minutes
[2]

10. Suggest three occupations that you would expect to involve a higher than normal
exposure to radiation. For each occupation, say why the radiation dose is increased.

1. ....

....

2. ....

....

3. ....

....
[3]

11. Explain why filament bulbs are not very energy-efficient.

....

....

....
[2]

15

Answers

B2a — Cells, Organs & Populations: Test 1

1. B
2. C
3. A
4. A
5. B
6. C
7. B
8. A
9. E.g. Bacterial cells don't contain a nucleus, whereas yeast cells do *(1 mark)*.
10. Cell differentiation is the process by which cells become specialised for a particular function *(1 mark)*.
11. Cellulose *(1 mark)*. The cell wall *(1 mark)*.
12. A — small intestine *(1 mark)*
    B — pancreas *(1 mark)*
    C — large intestine *(1 mark)*

B2a — Cells, Organs & Populations: Test 2

1. C
2. B
3. B
4. A
5. C
6. A
7. B
8. A
9. Some dissolved substances are too large to fit through the cell membrane, so cannot enter cells by diffusion *(1 mark)*.
10. E.g. It has a long tail / streamlined head to help it swim to an egg cell *(1 mark)*.
11. carbon dioxide + water $\xrightarrow{\text{sunlight}}$ glucose + oxygen

    (1 mark for one or two gaps filled correctly, 2 marks for whole equation completed correctly)
12. Mean — divide the total number of daisies counted by the number of samples/quadrats (5) *(1 mark)*.

    Median — list the number of daisies counted in each sample/quadrat in order of size *(1 mark)*. The median is the middle value *(1 mark)*.

B2a — Cells, Organs & Populations: Test 3

1. C
2. C
3. A
4. B
5. A
6. C
7. B
8. A
9. The small intestine absorbs soluble food molecules *(1 mark)* but the large intestine absorbs water from undigested food, leaving faeces *(1 mark)*.

10. A quadrat is a square frame enclosing a known area *(1 mark)*. E.g. The organisms within the frame can be counted and this number can be compared to data taken from quadrats in other places. *(1 mark)*.
11. E.g. Muscular tissue, to churn the stomach contents *(1 mark)*. Glandular tissue, to produce digestive juices *(1 mark)*. Epithelial tissue, to cover the outside and inside of the stomach *(1 mark)*.

B2a — Cells, Organs & Populations: Test 4

1. A
2. C
3. B
4. A
5. B
6. C
7. A
8. B
9. As the temperature increases, photosynthesis increases initially *(1 mark)*. After a point, the enzymes needed for photosynthesis are damaged (denatured) by the heat, so photosynthesis stops *(1 mark)*.
10.

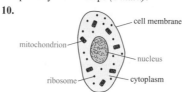

(1 mark for each correct label)
Mitochondria are where most of the reactions for respiration take place *(1 mark)*. Ribosomes are where protein synthesis takes place *(1 mark)*.
11. It moves across the cell membrane by diffusion *(1 mark)*.

B2a — Cells, Organs & Populations: Test 5

1. C
2. B
3. A
4. B
5. C
6. C
7. A
8. A
9. E.g. The salivary glands and the pancreas *(1 mark)*.
10. It will slow down *(1 mark)* because there will be less sunlight to provide light energy *(1 mark)*.
11. Glucose is combined with nitrate ions from the soil *(1 mark)* to make amino acids, which are made into proteins *(1 mark)*.

12. E.g. He could use quadrats to compare the number of daffodils in areas of the field *(1 mark)* with different conditions, e.g. in a shaded area and a sunny area *(1 mark)*. / He could use a transect to study how the number of daffodils varies across the field *(1 mark)* depending on the conditions, e.g. from next to a hedge to the middle of a field *(1 mark)*.

B2b — Enzymes & Genetics: Test 1

1. C
2. B
3. A
4. B
5. A
6. A
7. B
8. A
9. Although they play an important role in digestion, enzymes also control all the chemical reactions that take place inside cells *(1 mark)*.
10. Muscle fatigue is where the muscles tire and can no longer contract efficiently *(1 mark)*. It occurs when lactic acid builds up in the muscles during anaerobic respiration *(1 mark)*.
11. Any two of, e.g. Asexual reproduction. / Growth. / Repair or replacement of damaged cells. *(1 mark each)*
12. That characteristics are passed from one generation to the next *(1 mark)* by separately inherited factors which he named 'hereditary units' *(1 mark)*.

B2b — Enzymes & Genetics: Test 2

1. B
2. C
3. A
4. B
5. A
6. C
7. B
8. A
9. The Y chromosome causes male characteristics to develop *(1 mark)*.
10. Any two of, e.g. Destruction of habitat. / A new predator. / A new disease. / Competition with another, more successful species for resources. / A catastrophic event, e.g. a volcanic eruption. / The development of new species through speciation. *(1 mark each)*
11. The plant will be tall *(1 mark)*, as the tall allele (T) is dominant over the recessive dwarf allele (t) *(1 mark)*.

Answers

12. DNA fingerprinting is a process used to identify individuals from their DNA *(1 mark)*, based on the fact that everyone's DNA is unique *(1 mark)*.

B2b — Enzymes & Genetics: Test 3

1.	C	2.	C
3.	B	4.	B
5.	A	6.	C
7.	A	8.	A

9. The enzyme's unique shape changes *(1 mark)*. As an enzyme's shape is essential to its function, it won't work any more *(1 mark)*.

10. The process in which cells are removed from an embryo and checked to see if the embryo will suffer from certain genetic disorders *(1 mark)*.

11. Fossils are the remains or impressions of plants and animals that were alive many years ago *(1 mark)*.

12. Each population has a range of alleles that control their characteristics *(1 mark)*. If there are different conditions on either side of the flood, different characteristics will become more common in each population due to natural selection *(1 mark)*. Eventually individuals from each population will become so different that they will no longer be able to interbreed successfully *(1 mark)*.

B2b — Enzymes & Genetics: Test 4

1.	C	2.	A
3.	B	4.	A
5.	C	6.	B
7.	A	8.	A

9.

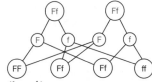

(1 mark)
As the cystic fibrosis gene is recessive, for the child to be a sufferer they will need two recessive alleles *(1 mark)*. The diagram shows that the chance the child will suffer from cystic fibrosis is 25%, or 1 in 4 *(1 mark)*.

10. Where populations of a species become separated *(1 mark)*.

11. E.g. Stem cells may be used to cure many diseases *(1 mark)*. Some people believe that preventing the suffering of a living person is more important than protecting the rights of embryos *(1 mark)*. The embryos used in research are usually unwanted ones from fertility clinics, so this puts them to good use, rather than letting them go to waste *(1 mark)*.

B2b — Enzymes & Genetics: Test 5

1.	C	2.	B
3.	B	4.	A
5.	C	6.	C
7.	A	8.	B

9. Alex is a boy *(1 mark)*. (Females have two X chromosomes, males have an X and a Y chromosome.)

10. Protease enzymes catalyse the breakdown of proteins into amino acids in the stomach *(1 mark)*.

11. Any two of, e.g. To build up larger molecules (e.g. proteins) from smaller ones. / In animals, to allow muscles to contract. / In mammals and birds, to keep the body temperature steady. / In plants, to build sugars, nitrates and other nutrients into amino acids. *(1 mark each)*

12. During sexual reproduction two gametes fuse together, producing a new cell *(1 mark)*. This cell contains a mixture of chromosomes — some from the mother, and some from the father *(1 mark)*. This means it inherits a combination of features from each parent, producing variation *(1 mark)*.

C2a — Bonding & Calculations: Test 1

1.	A	2.	B
3.	B	4.	B
5.	A	6.	A
7.	B	8.	B

9. Giant covalent / macromolecular *(1 mark)*.

10. Relative formula mass (M_r)
= 24 + (2 × 16) + (2 × 1) = 58 *(1 mark)*
Number of moles = Mass ÷ M_r
= 145 g ÷ 58 *(1 mark)*
= 2.5 moles *(1 mark)*
(Or 3 marks for the correct answer via any other method.)

11. Fullerenes are nanoparticles *(1 mark)*. They are molecules of carbon atoms arranged in hexagonal rings *(1 mark)*. They are used e.g. for drug delivery into the body / in lubricants / as catalysts / in nanotubes for reinforcing materials *(1 mark)*.

C2a — Bonding & Calculations: Test 2

1.	B	2.	C
3.	A	4.	A
5.	A	6.	B
7.	B	8.	B

9. Protons and neutrons both have a relative mass of 1. The relative mass of an electron is very small *(1 mark)*.

10. An ionic compound has a giant ionic lattice structure *(1 mark)* that's held together by electrostatic forces of attraction *(1 mark)* between the oppositely charged ions *(1 mark)*.

11. Relative formula mass (M_r)
= (2 × 12) + (6 × 1) + 16 = 46 *(1 mark)*
Percentage mass =
100 × (A_r × number of atoms) ÷ M_r
= 100 × (12 × 2) ÷ 46 *(1 mark)*
= 52% (to the nearest whole number) *(1 mark)*
(Or 3 marks for the correct answer via any other method.)

C2a — Bonding & Calculations: Test 3

1.	B	2.	C
3.	A	4.	B
5.	C	6.	B
7.	A	8.	A

9. A Cl_2 molecule contains 2 chlorine atoms joined by a single covalent bond *(1 mark)*. Each chlorine atom has 7 electrons in its outer shell. By forming a covalent bond and sharing a pair of electrons, the outer shell of each atom is full *(1 mark)*.

10. The balanced equation is: $C + O_2 \rightarrow CO_2$
Relative formula mass (M_r) of CO_2
= 12 + (2 × 16) = 44 *(1 mark)*
For every 12 g of C reacting there are 44 g of CO_2 produced.
So 66 g of C produces
(66 × 44 ÷ 12) g of CO_2 *(1 mark)*
= 242 g of CO_2 *(1 mark)*.
(Or 3 marks for the correct answer via any other method.)

Answers

11. Nanoparticles are tiny particles which are 1-100 nanometres in size, containing roughly a few hundred atoms *(1 mark)*. They can be used for e.g. industrial catalysts / highly specific sensors / stronger, lighter building materials / cosmetics / nanomedicine / lubricant coatings / electrical circuits in computer chips *(1 mark)*.

C2a — Bonding & Calculations: Test 4

1. A
2. B
3. B
4. A
5. C
6. C
7. A
8. A

9. Isotopes are different atoms of the same element, which have the same number of protons but different numbers of neutrons *(1 mark)*.

10. Percentage yield =
(actual yield ÷ predicted yield) × 100
= (36 ÷ 50) × 100 *(1 mark)*
= 72% *(1 mark)*
(Or 2 marks for the correct answer via any other method.)
It could be less than 100% because e.g. the reaction might be reversible and so the reactants will never be completely converted to products / some product might have been lost when it was separated from the reaction mixture / another unexpected reaction might have happened which used up some of the reactants *(1 mark)*.

11. Oxygen is a simple molecular substance with no overall electric charge, so there are no ions to conduct electricity *(1 mark)*. Graphite is made of layers of carbon atoms that each form only three covalent bonds *(1 mark)*. It conducts electricity because each carbon atom has one delocalised electron that is free to move throughout the structure *(1 mark)*.

C2a — Bonding & Calculations: Test 5

1. A
2. C
3. B
4. A
5. C
6. B
7. A
8. B

9. Dividing the reacting mass by the A_r for each element gives:
Fe: 140 g ÷ 56 = 2.5
O: 40 g ÷ 16 = 2.5 *(1 mark)*
For every 2.5 atoms of Fe reacting there are 2.5 atoms of O. This can be simplified to a 1:1 ratio of Fe to O reacting *(1 mark)*.
So the empirical formula is FeO *(1 mark)*.
(Or 3 marks for the correct answer via any other method.)

10. The different substances in the gas move through a column packed with a solid material at different speeds, so they become separated and arrive at the detector at different times *(1 mark)*. A gas chromatograph is produced, on which the number of peaks shows the number of different substances present *(1 mark)* and the position of the peaks shows the retention time of each substance (the time taken for that substance to reach the detector) *(1 mark)*. The gas chromatography column can be linked to a mass spectrometer, which gives the relative molecular mass (M_r) of each substance from the molecular ion peak *(1 mark)*.

C2b — Rates, Salts & Electrolysis: Test 1

1. A
2. A
3. B
4. A
5. B
6. C
7. A
8. B

9. E.g. Experiment 2 could have been carried out at a higher temperature / with a greater concentration of reactants / at a higher pressure (with gases) / with a catalyst / with solid reactants crushed into smaller parts to give them a greater surface area *(1 mark)*. This would have increased the rate of reaction, as shown by the steeper graph *(1 mark)*.

10. A metal salt *(1 mark)* and hydrogen *(1 mark)*.

11. It's endothermic *(1 mark)*. Endothermic reactions take in energy from the surroundings *(1 mark)*. A substance has to take in energy through heating to thermally decompose *(1 mark)*.

C2b — Rates, Salts & Electrolysis: Test 2

1. B
2. A
3. A
4. B
5. C
6. B
7. B
8. B

9. $H^+_{(aq)} + OH^-_{(aq)} \rightarrow H_2O_{(l)}$ *(1 mark)*

10. Bases can be soluble or insoluble. An alkali is a soluble base *(1 mark)*.

11. Hydrogen *(1 mark)* and chlorine *(1 mark)*.

12. Increasing the concentration of a solution increases the number of reactant particles in a given volume *(1 mark)* so will increase the frequency of successful collisions *(1 mark)*. The more successful collisions in a given time, the faster the reaction rate *(1 mark)*.

C2b — Rates, Salts & Electrolysis: Test 3

1. B
2. C
3. B
4. B
5. C
6. A
7. A
8. A

9. Copper chloride *(1 mark)* and water *(1 mark)*.

10. In a precipitation reaction, two solutions are reacted together to form a different solution plus an insoluble salt *(1 mark)*. The salt 'precipitates out' — which means it forms as a solid, causing the solution to become cloudy / opaque *(1 mark)*.

11. E.g. Carry out the experiment on a mass balance and record the decrease in mass *(1 mark)* and the time it takes for the reaction to finish *(1 mark)*. Calculate the rate of reaction by dividing the decrease in mass by the time taken *(1 mark)*. / Using a gas syringe, record the volume of gas given off *(1 mark)* and the time it takes for the reaction to finish *(1 mark)*. Calculate the rate of reaction by dividing the volume of gas by the time taken *(1 mark)*.

C2b — Rates, Salts & Electrolysis: Test 4

1. C
2. B
3. A
4. A
5. C
6. B
7. B
8. A

Answers

9. A neutralisation reaction occurs *(1 mark)* and a salt and water are formed *(1 mark)*.

10. Catalysts speed up reactions, so the plant doesn't need to operate for as long to produce the same amount of product *(1 mark)*. Some reactions don't need such high temperatures if a catalyst is used, so energy costs are reduced *(1 mark)*.

11. Ammonia is dissolved in water to make an alkaline solution *(1 mark)*. This is reacted with an acid *(1 mark)* to produce ammonium salts *(1 mark)* which can be used as fertiliser.

C2b — Rates, Salts & Electrolysis: Test 5

1. A
2. B
3. B
4. A
5. C
6. B
7. B
8. A

9. Oxidation is the loss of electrons, whereas reduction is the gain of electrons *(1 mark)*.

10. The total volume of O_2 produced will stay the same whether there is a catalyst or not *(1 mark)*. Only the rate of O_2 production will change / the total volume of O_2 produced is only affected by the initial amount of H_2O_2 *(1 mark)*.

11. At the negative electrode, aluminium ions are reduced/gain electrons to form aluminium *(1 mark)*. At the positive electrode, oxygen ions are oxidised/ lose electrons to form oxygen *(1 mark)*. The oxygen reacts with the carbon in the electrode to produce carbon dioxide *(1 mark)*. This 'wears away' the positive electrode *(1 mark)*.

P2a — Motion, Energy & Electricity: Test 1

1. B
2. A
3. A
4. B
5. C
6. C
7. B
8. A

9. Between points A and B, the object slows to a stop *(1 mark)*. Then between points B and C, the object is stationary *(1 mark)*.

10. They both have variable resistance *(1 mark)*, but the resistance of an LDR changes with light and the resistance of a thermistor changes with temperature *(1 mark)*.

11. 2 mins = $2 \times 60 = 120$ s *(1 mark)*
Rearrange the formula:
energy transferred
    = power × time taken
    = 50×120 *(1 mark)*
    = 6000 J *(1 mark)*
(Or 3 marks for the correct answer via any other method.)

P2a — Motion, Energy & Electricity: Test 2

1. B
2. B
3. A
4. B
5. C
6. C
7. B
8. A

9. When she pushed the wall, she experienced an equal force <u>from</u> the wall pushing her backwards. So, assuming no friction, both forces are equal to mass × acceleration:
$60 \times 3 = 180$ N *(1 mark)*

10. The object initially accelerates due to gravity *(1 mark)*. When the frictional forces increase enough to match the force of gravity, the resultant force on the object is zero *(1 mark)* and so it moves at terminal velocity (steady speed) *(1 mark)*.

11. As more current flows through the lamp, the temperature of the filament increases *(1 mark)*. As the temperature increases, the resistance increases *(1 mark)*. The greater the resistance, the flatter the graph, so the graph curves as the current increases *(1 mark)*.

P2a — Motion, Energy & Electricity: Test 3

1. A
2. B
3. B
4. B
5. A
6. C
7. B
8. A

9.
(1 mark for each correct section)

10. 500 g = 0.5 kg *(1 mark)*
Rearrange the formula:
change in height = change in gravitational potential energy ÷ (mass × g)
= $100 \div (0.5 \times 10)$ *(1 mark)*
= 20 m *(1 mark)*
(Or 3 marks for the correct answer via any other method.)

11. In a parallel circuit, each component is connected separately to the power supply *(1 mark)*. When one bulb blows, only that part of the circuit is broken — the part connecting the other bulb to the power supply is fine, so the light stays on *(1 mark)*.

P2a — Motion, Energy & Electricity: Test 4

1. B
2. C
3. A
4. B
5. A
6. A
7. B
8. A

9. In a series circuit, the supply potential difference is shared, so:
$V_3 = V_1 + V_2 = 3 + 2 = 5$ V *(1 mark)*
Resistances add up, so:
$R = R_1 + R_2 = 6 + 4 = 10\ \Omega$ *(1 mark)*
The current is calculated using the supply potential difference and the total resistance of the circuit.
Rearrange the formula:
current = p.d. ÷ resistance
    = $V_3 \div R$ *(1 mark)*
    = $5 \div 10 = 0.5$ A
(1 mark for an answer correctly calculated using the values of V_3 and R worked out earlier in the question.)
(Or 2 marks for the correct current via any other method.)

10. $1000 - 400 = 600$ N *(1 mark)*

11. The speed is given by the gradient.
Gradient = $10 \div 2$ *(1 mark)*
    = 5 m/s *(1 mark)*
(Or 2 marks for the correct answer via any other method.)

P2a — Motion, Energy & Electricity: Test 5

1. B
2. C
3. B
4. A
5. C
6. A
7. B
8. A

Answers

9. As the gun was stationary, the total momentum before it was fired was zero. This means the gun's momentum after must be equal and opposite to the bullet's momentum after *(1 mark)*.
Bullet momentum = 0.1 × 100
    = 10 kg m/s *(1 mark)*
So gun momentum is −10 kg m/s.
Rearrange the formula:
velocity = momentum ÷ mass
    = −10 ÷ 2 *(1 mark)*
    = −5 m/s
So recoil speed is 5 m/s *(1 mark)*.
(Or 4 marks for the correct answer via any other method.)

10. When the materials are rubbed together, negatively charged electrons are rubbed off one material and move onto the other *(1 mark)*. This leaves the material they've moved off with a positive charge, and the material they've moved onto with an equal negative charge *(1 mark)*.

11. Make its shape more streamlined / reduce drag *(1 mark)*.

P2b — Electricity & the Atom: Test 1

1.	C	2.	C
3.	A	4.	B
5.	A	6.	C
7.	B	8.	B

9. A Residual Current Circuit Breaker (RCCB) detects a difference in current between the live and neutral wires *(1 mark)* and opens a switch to cut off the power to the appliance *(1 mark)*.

10. The time period is shown by the horizontal distance between two peaks on the trace — 5 divisions *(1 mark)*. Multiply by the timebase setting:
time period = 5 × 0.005 s = 0.025 s *(1 mark)*
frequency = 1 ÷ time period
= 1 ÷ 0.025 = 40 Hz *(1 mark)*
(Or 3 marks for the correct answer via any other method.)

11. Alpha and beta *(1 mark)*.

12. An atom is electrically neutral, but an ion is charged. / An atom has the same number of protons and electrons, but an ion doesn't *(1 mark)*.

P2b — Electricity & the Atom: Test 2

1.	C	2.	B
3.	B	4.	B
5.	A	6.	B
7.	B	8.	B

9. Any two of, e.g. As medical tracers (injected into/swallowed by a patient to help with diagnosis). / To sterilise surgical instruments. / To treat cancer (in radiotherapy). *(1 mark each)*

10. Convert 2 hours into seconds:
2 × 60 × 60 = 7200 s *(1 mark)*.
Rearrange the formula:
energy transferred = power × time
= 15 × 7200 *(1 mark)*
= 108 000 J *(1 mark)*
(Or 3 marks for the correct answer via any other method.)

11. $^{32}_{16}$S
(1 mark for each correct number)

P2b — Electricity & the Atom: Test 3

1.	C	2.	A
3.	A	4.	B
5.	C	6.	A
7.	A	8.	B

9. The answer is 4 hours.
(2 marks for a correct answer including units, or 1 mark for an attempt to halve the initial activity on the vertical axis of the graph.)

10. Convert energy into J:
3 kJ = 3000 J *(1 mark)*
Rearrange the formula:
charge = energy ÷ p.d.
    = 3000 ÷ 1.5 *(1 mark)*
    = 2000 C *(1 mark)*
(Or 3 marks for the correct answer via any other method.)

11. Any two of, e.g. Radioactive waste is produced, which is difficult to dispose of safely. / It's expensive to set up and close down nuclear power stations. / There is a risk of radiation leaks and catastrophes. *(1 mark each)*

P2b — Electricity & the Atom: Test 4

1.	B	2.	A
3.	B	4.	A
5.	C	6.	A
7.	A	8.	B

9. 1. alpha
2. gamma
3. beta
(2 marks for all three correct, 1 mark for one or two correct)

10. Nuclear fusion creates a force outwards that balances the gravity pulling everything inwards *(1 mark)*. There is so much hydrogen in a star, that the fusion can last for millions of years in this stable phase *(1 mark)*.

11. Rearrange the formula:
current = power ÷ potential difference
    = 150 ÷ 230 *(1 mark)*
    = 0.65 A *(1 mark)*
A 1A fuse would be suitable *(1 mark)*.

P2b — Electricity & the Atom: Test 5

1.	B	2.	A
3.	B	4.	B
5.	C	6.	A
7.	B	8.	A

9. Keep halving the initial count rate until it is at the level required:
600 ÷ 2 = 300
300 ÷ 2 = 150
150 ÷ 2 = 75
Count how many times you had to halve it (3) *(1 mark)*, and multiply this number by the half-life of the sample:
3 × 30 = 90 minutes *(1 mark)*
(Or 2 marks for the correct answer via any other method.)

10. Any three of, e.g. Miner – surrounded by rocks and/or gases that emit radiation. / Radiographer – works in hospital using ionising radiation to treat patients. / Pilot – at high altitudes, there are more cosmic rays. / Nuclear industry worker – works directly with radioactive materials. *(1 mark each)*

11. Filaments glow because they get hot *(1 mark)*, which means they waste a lot of electrical energy as heat instead of using it to make useful light *(1 mark)*.